THE CELLO ETUDE SYSTEM

Part 1A:
Closed First Position
DUET BOOK

compiled and written
by Cassia Harvey
with accompaniments
by Myanna Harvey

Grateful thanks to cellist and teacher Emily Rodgers (www.celloemily.com)
for her help in preparing this manuscript for publication!

CHP413

www.charveypublications.com - print books
www.learnstrings.com - downloadable books
www.harveystringarrangements.com - chamber music

Table of Contents

What's In the Book

Rare and Classic Cello Etudes

Many of these etudes are extremely rare while others are well-known classic cello studies by the great teachers of the past. The etudes have been put in approximate order of difficulty and grouped so that they teach and review essential cello skills.

Two Paths Through the Book

- *Relaxed Learners* can play through the book as written.
- *Accelerated Learners* can use the guides at the bottom of the etudes to chart a faster course.

The Purpose of Etudes

Etudes are a bridge between exercises and repertoire, incorporating both technique and musicality to teach one or more specific skills. Because technical exercises often fall short in teaching rhythm, dynamics, etc., **etudes are an essential part of every practice session.** The duet parts to these etudes let the teacher lead rhythmically and expressively and help their student learn the skills they will need to play in chamber groups or orchestras.

How This Series Got Started

When I started teaching, I used all of the well-known cello etude books with my students, including Dotzauer, Schroeder, and Lee. But over the years, I was surprised to find just how many more amazing etudes had been written! These etudes were unknown, out of print, and almost impossible to find. I started collecting etudes, making copies, and distributing them to my students. As my studio room started filling up with all of these books, I realized that I was assigning just a few etudes from each book before moving to another book. This just wasn't practical and certainly wasn't replicable to other teaching studios. So I started compiling the etudes, grouping them by skill, and putting them in order of difficulty (as much as possible.) I wanted this series to be both a *resource* and a *practical system* through the etudes that my students and I have been studying for many years. The relaxed and accelerated learning paths can accommodate students with different learning styles and the teacher is encouraged to further chart their own path through each book with their students.

How to Practice Using This Book

- Etudes should be practiced after exercises and scales and before repertoire.
- This book consists of short etudes at or close to the same level, only incrementally increasing in difficulty. *Because of this, teachers may assign multiple etudes each week.* This book was designed to be studied at a somewhat quicker pace than most other etude books.
- By playing through multiple etudes each week, **students will build essential sight-reading skills** from the very beginning.
- Relaxed learners can play through the entire book. Accelerated learners should use the cues below the etudes to chart their path through the book. See below for more about the accelerated path.

Accelerated Etude Path

- Students who learn more quickly, who are on an advanced learning trajectory, or who have easily mastered the material should use the accelerated learning path.
- The accelerated learning path teaches the same concepts as the relaxed learning path but has less review and repetition.
- If you are unsure whether the relaxed or accelerated path is right for you, start on the relaxed path and switch to the accelerated path if the etudes start to feel too easy.

Book 1A: Goals for Study

Fluently play the notes in closed first position at various speeds.

Play complex slurs and ties, including syncopation across the barline.

Learn rhythms in 4/4, 3/4, 2/4, 6/8, 3/8, 3/2, and 5/4 time signatures.

Learn dotted quarter note and dotted eighth note rhythms.

Play trills, grace notes, and mordents.

Play double stops in etudes, listening for intonation and smooth tone.

Incorporate dynamics in etudes.

Work on chamber music skills such as entrances and coordinating with another player (duet book only.)

☐ = Accelerated Path

Complete List of Etudes - Page 1

Etude	Title	Composer	Solo Page	Duet Page
1	C Major Scale Patterns	Nölck, A.	2	2
2	C Major Arpeggio Patterns	Depas, E.	2	3
3	C Major Double Stop Etudes	Javelot, J.	3	4
4	Smooth Broken Thirds	Kummer, F.	3	5
5	Building a Graceful and Rhythmic Bow	Nölck, A.	4	6
6	Slow Up-Bows in 3/4	Kummer, F.	5	8
7	Slurs Across the Barline	Gruet, A.	5	9
8	Bow Speed Etude	Bréval, J.	6	9
9	Staccato Etude	Reinagle, J.	6	10
10	6/8 Preparatory Etude	Harvey, C.	7	11
11	Rhythm in 6/8	Schiffer, A.	7	12
12	Trading the Melody	Stiastny, B.	8	13
13	Tone-Building Etude	Reinagle, J.	8	14
14	Bow Rhythms	Quarenghi, G.	10	16
15	Broken Thirds and Counting Half Notes	Van Rooijen, N.	11	18
16	Skipping Notes Across Strings for Speed	Schröder, C.	11	19
17	Melodic Etude for Expression	Malkin, J.	12	20
18	Lyrical Slur Study	Malkin, J.	13	22
19	String Crossing in Slurs	Gruet, A.	14	24
20	G Major Scale	Harvey, C.	14	24
21	Introduction to G Major	Javelot, J.	14	25
22	Slurs Across Strings	Lee, S.	15	26
23	Double Stop Etude in G Major	Harvey, C.	16	27
24	Rhythmic Entrances	Uberti, V.	16	28
25	Dotted Half Notes and More Entrances	Charpentier, A.	17	29
26	Preparatory Exercise for No. 27	Harvey, C.	18	30
27	String Crossing	Lee, S.	18	31
28	"Fiddle Bowing" and Chords	Harvey, C.	19	32
29	Left and Right-Hand Agility	Van Rooijen, N.	20	33
30	Slur Combinations with Light Staccato	Lee, S.	20	34

☐ = Accelerated
Path

☐ = Accelerated Path

Complete List of Etudes - Page 3

☐ = Accelerated
Path

Etude	Title	Composer	Solo Page	Duet Page
91	Melodic Study	Benito, C. de	66	107
92	Dotted Eighths in 3/4 Timing	Cuccoli, A.	66	108
93	Finger Agility Study	Cuccoli, A.	67	110
94	Agility Study	Alexander, J.	68	111
95	Fugal Study	Nölck, A.	69	112
96	Study on Precise Entrances	Van Rooijen, N.	70	114
97	Study on Pickup Notes	Cuccoli, A.	71	116
98	Trill Study	Harvey, C.	72	118
99	Embellishment Study	Harvey, C.	72	119
100	Melodic Study in 6/8	Gross, J. B.	73	120
101	String Crossing Study	Lee, S.	74	121
102	Triplet Study	Lee, S.	74	122
103	Agility Study	Paschalski, K.	75	123
104	Focus on Playing Even Notes	Kummer, F.	76	124
105	Bow Agility Study	Davidov, K.	77	126
106	String Crossing Etude	Davidov, K.	78	128
107	String Crossing	Nölck, A.	79	130
108a	Melodic Etude with Rhythmic Accompaniment	Popper, D.	80	132
108b	Melodic Etude as Originally Written	Popper, D.	80	134
109	Learning to Slur and Hold Double Stops	Borshitzky, J.	82	136
110a	Double Stop Etude, Stage One	Popper, D.	84	138
110b	Double Stop Etude, Stage Two	Popper, D.	85	140
110c	Double Stop Etude, Stage Three	Popper, D.	86	142
110d	Double Stop Etude, Stage Four	Popper, D.	87	144
110e	Double Stop Etude, Stage Five - As Written	Popper, D.	88	146

Part One: C Major Studies

1. C Major Scale Patterns

A. Nölck
Duet by M. Harvey, after A. Nölck

2. C Major Arpeggio Patterns

E. Depas
Duet by M. Harvey

3. C Major Double Stop Etude

J. Javelot, arr. C. Harvey
Duet by M. Harvey

Accelerated students may skip to No. 8.

4. Smooth Broken Thirds

F. Kummer

5. Building a Graceful and Rhythmic Bow

A. Nölck
Duet by M. Harvey after A. Nölck

Andante con moto

6. Slow Up-Bows in 3/4

F. Kummer, arr. C. Harvey

7. Slurs Across the Barline

A. Gruet
Duet by M. Harvey

8. Bow Speed Etude

J. Bréval, arr. C. Harvey

9. Staccato Etude

J. Reinagle, arr. C. Harvey
Duet by M. Harvey

Accelerated students may skip to No. 11.

10. 6/8 Preparatory Etude

C. Harvey
Duet by M. Harvey

11. Rhythm in 6/8

A. Schiffer, arr. C. Harvey

12. Trading the Melody

B. Stiastny, arr. C. Harvey

13. Tone-Building Etude

J. Reinagle, arr. C. Harvey
Duet by M. Harvey

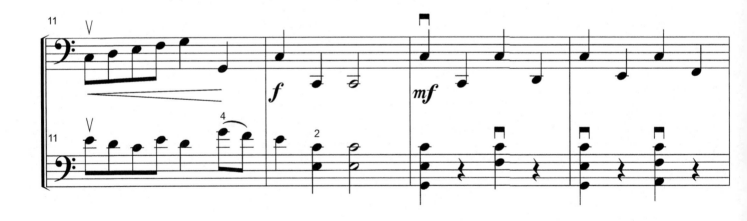

As smooth as possible;
keep bow on the string!

Accelerated students may skip to No. 16.

14. Bow Rhythms

G. Quarenghi, arr. C. Harvey
Duet by M. Harvey

15. Broken Thirds and Counting Half Notes

N. Van Rooijen, arr. C. Harvey

16. Skipping Notes Across Strings for Speed

C. Schröder

II

17. Melodic Etude for Expression

J. Malkin, arr. C. Harvey
Duet by M. Harvey

18. Lyrical Slur Study

J. Malkin, arr. C. Harvey
Duet by M. Harvey

111111

1111111

Accelerated students may skip to No. 21.

19. String Crossing in Slurs

A. Gruet
Duet by M. Harvey

Part Two: G Major Studies

20. G Major Scale

C. Harvey

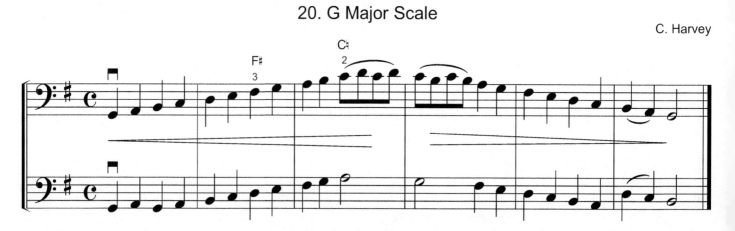

21. Introduction to G Major

J. Javelot, arr. C. Harvey
Duet by M. Harvey

Accelerated students may skip to No. 23.

22. Slurs Across Strings

S. Lee

23. Double Stop Etude in G Major

C. Harvey
Duet by M. Harvey

Accelerated students may skip to No. 25.

The student should listen to their
instructor and imitate the dynamic
that the instructor has just played.

24. Rhythmic Entrances

V. Uberti

25. Dotted Half Notes and More Entrances

A. Charpentier

Moderato

Rall. poco a poco

Accelerated students may skip to No. 27.

26. Preparatory Exercise for No. 27

Note: This practice exercise shows
you how to balance the bow and
curve your left-hand fingers for Etude 27.

C. Harvey
Duet by M. Harvey

27. String Crossing

S. Lee
Duet arranged by M. Harvey

Accelerated students may skip to No. 30.

28. "Fiddle Bowing" and Chords

C. Harvey
Duet by M. Harvey

Part Three: Bow Agility

29. Left and Right-Hand Agility

N. Van Rooijen, arr. C. Harvey

Allegro

30. Slur Combinations with Light Staccato

S. Lee

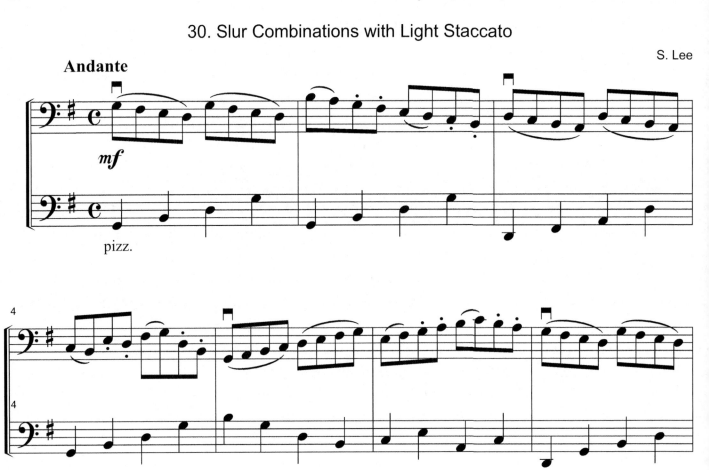

31. Eighth Note Slurs in 3/4 Timing

J. Malkin, arr. C.Harvey
Duet by M. Harvey

32. Slurs Across the Barline

S. Lee

Accelerated students may skip to No. 34.

33. Triplet Etude

S. Lee
Duet by M. Harvey

34. Triplets and Eighth Notes

J. Borshitzky, arr. C. Harvey

35. Even Tone on Uneven Slur Patterns

Note: Don't play the single note louder than the slurred notes.
Lighten the bow pressure on the single note to make up for the faster bow speed.

J. F. Dotzauer

Accelerated students may skip to No. 38.

Part Four: Dotted Quarter Notes

36. Dotted Quarter Note Rhythms

C. Harvey
Duet by M. Harvey

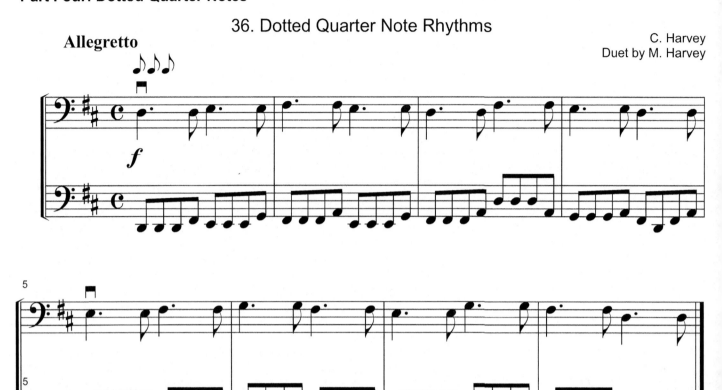

37. Dotted Quarter Note Study

C. Harvey
Duet by M. Harvey

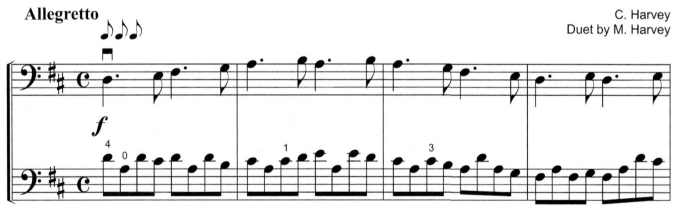

38. Dotted Quarter Note Etude in C Major

C. Lebouc, arr. C. Harvey

Moderato

Accelerated students may skip to No. 41.

39. Introduction to F Major

C. Harvey
Duet by M. Harvey

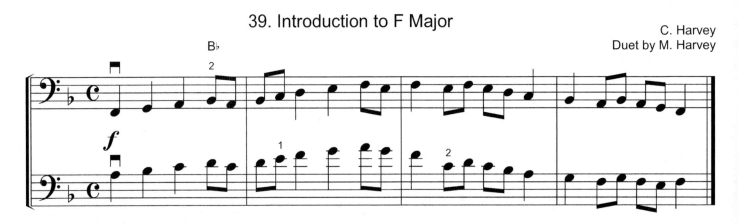

40. Dotted Quarter Notes on Lower Strings

D. S. McCosh
Duet by M. Harvey

Allegretto

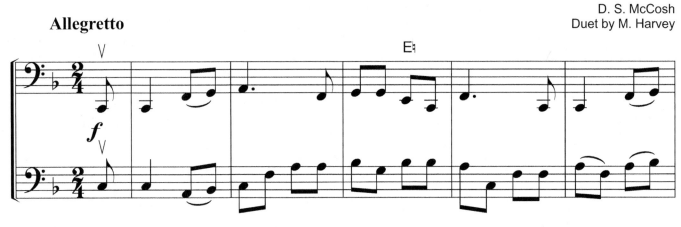

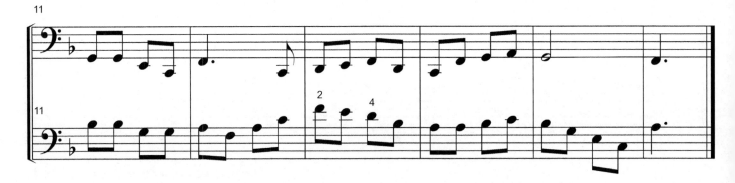

41. Double Stop Etude

C. Harvey
Duet by M. Harvey

42. Rhythm Pattern Study

A. Gruet
Duet by M. Harvey

43. Dotted Quarter Notes Outside Slurs

C. Fuchs
Duet by M. Harvey

Accelerated students may skip to No. 46.

44. Dotted Quarter Notes Inside Slurs

J. Werner

45. F Major Rhythm Etude

J. de Swert, arr. C. Harvey

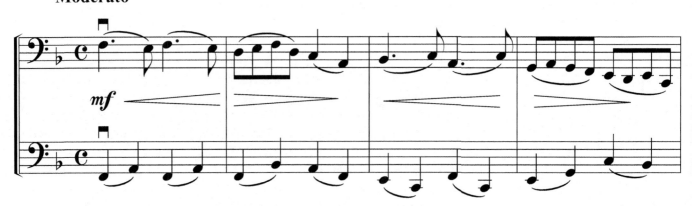

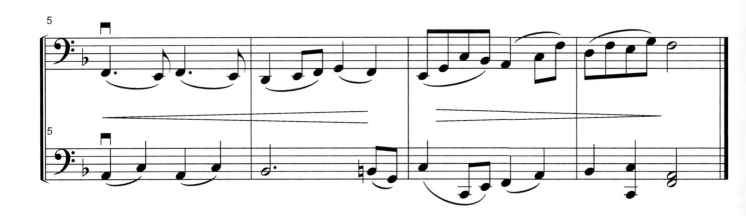

46. Phrasing with Dotted Quarter Notes

N. Van Rooijen, arr. C. Harvey

47. Bow Speed Etude

C. de Beriot, arr. C. Harvey
Duet by M. Harvey

Moderato

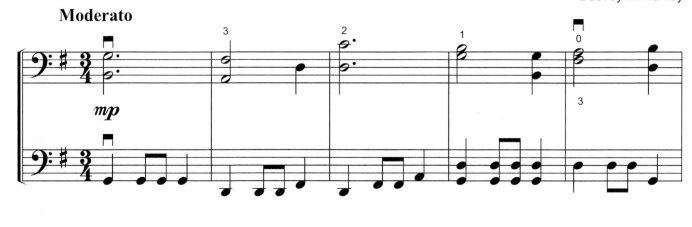

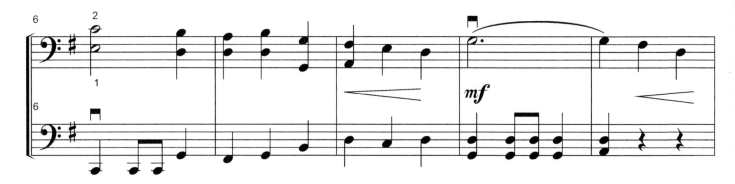

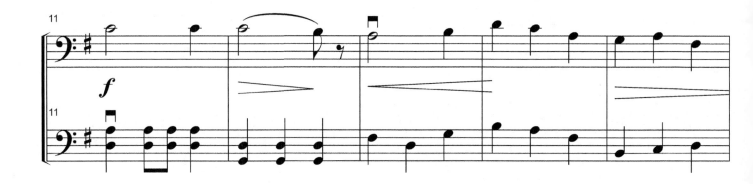

Accelerated students may skip to No. 50.

48. Subdividing Dotted Quarter Notes

C. Harvey

49. Study for Precise Rhythm

N. Van Rooijen, arr. C. Harvey

50. String Crossing Study

C. Harvey
Duet by M. Harvey

♩ = 100-120

51. Bow Agility Etude

K. Davidov

Andante

Accelerated students may skip to No. 53.

52. Study on Phrasing

C. Liégeois, arr. C. Harvey

53. Working on a Smooth Bow

W. H. Squire, Duet by M. Harvey

Part Five: Rhythm and Agility

54. Introduction to Tied Notes

A. Gruet
Duet by M. Harvey

55. Tied Note Study

N. Van Rooijen

Accelerated students may skip to No. 58.

56. Even Rhythm in 6/8

C. Harvey
Duet by M. Harvey

57. Agility Etude - For Speed!

J. B. Gross

Note: Have your left hand notes in place
before you play each down bow slur.

58. Arpeggios Across Strings

S. Lee

Allegretto

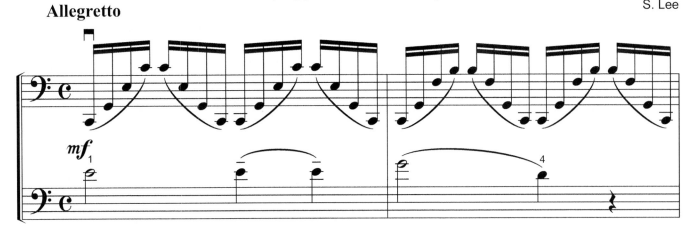

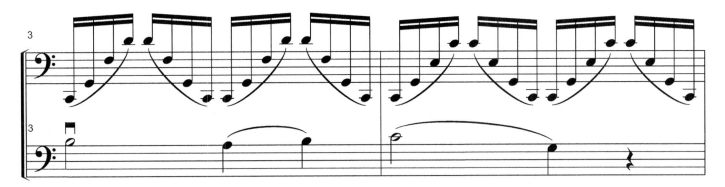

Flatten or "bar" finger
across the two strings.

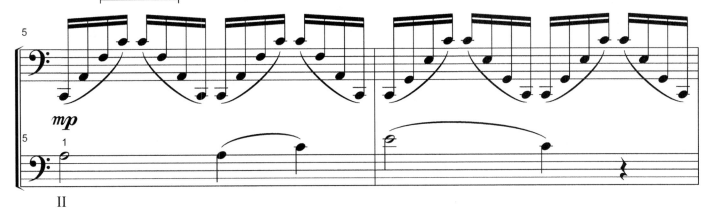

II

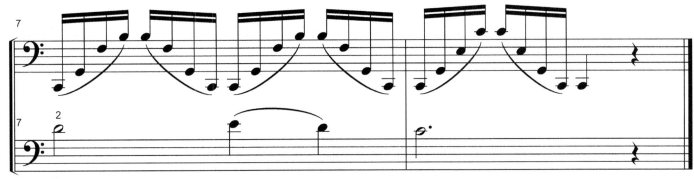

I

59. Off-Beat Slurs

J. de Swert
Duet by M. Harvey

60. Double Stop Etude

C. Harvey
Duet by M. Harvey

61. Slurs in 6/8

J. Werner
Duet by M. Harvey

II

Accelerated students may skip to No. 67.

62. 5/4 Timing

M. Harvey

63. C Major Study

J. B. Gross

Allegro vivace

64. Rhythmic Etude

C. Harvey
Duet by M. Harvey

65. Double Stop Study

C. Harvey
Duet by M. Harvey

66. Preparatory String Crossing Exercise

C. Harvey
Duet by M. Harvey

67. String Crossing Study

S. Lee

Flatten or "bar"
finger here.

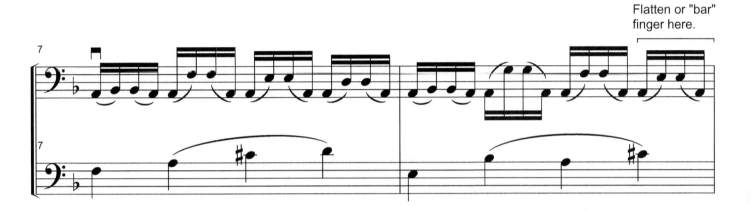

Flatten or "bar"
finger here.

simile

Accelerated students may skip to No. 70.

68. Pizzicato Etude

J. Tillière
Duet by M. Harvey

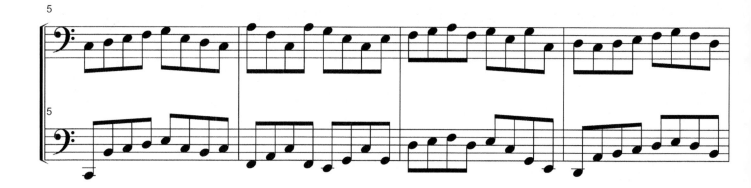

69. Syncopation Etude

B. Stiastny, arr. C. Harvey

Allegretto

70. Using Syncopation in Context

G. Kastner
Duet by M. Harvey

71. Double Stop March

C. Harvey
Duet by M. Harvey

72. Rhythmic Study on a Scale

J. MacDonald

73. String Crossing Etude

G. Quarenghi
Duet by M. Harvey

74. Rhythmic Etude

G. Kastner
Duet by M. Harvey

Accelerated students may skip to No. 76.

75. Focus on Staccato and Ties

B. Stiastny

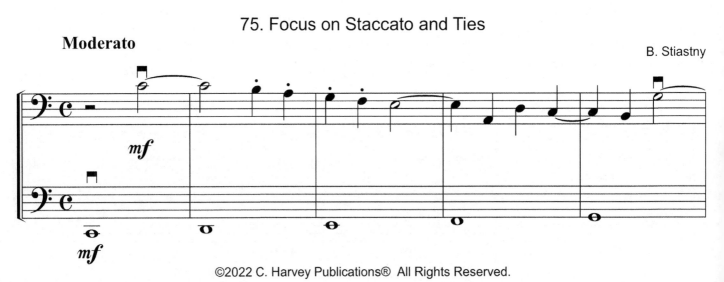

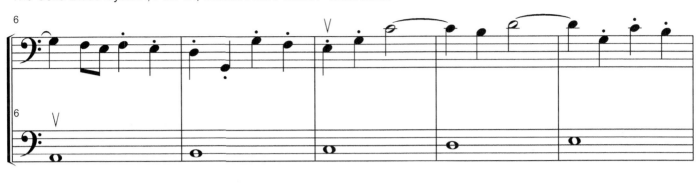

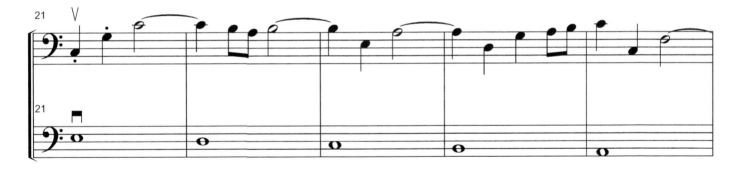

76. Longer Slurs in 6/8

A. Gruet
Duet by M. Harvey

Note: Mordents are articulations that have you play the written note, the next note above in the scale, and the written note again.

77. Study on Mordents

C. Harvey
Duet by M. Harvey

Moderato

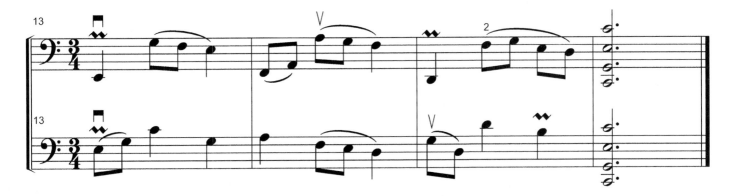

78. Lyrical Study for Smooth Bowing

J. Werner
Duet by M. Harvey

79. C Major Staccato Study

P. Vidal
Duet by M. Harvey

80. Bow Agility Study

L. Albrecht
Duet by M. Harvey

Accelerated students may skip to No. 83.

81. Bowing Variations Etude

L. Albrecht
Duet by M. Harvey

Part Six: Dotted Eighth Note Rhythms

82. Rhythms in Context

G. Kastner, arr. C. Harvey
Duet by M. Harvey

83. Melodic Study

C. Baudiot, arr. C. Harvey

Accelerated students may skip to No. 85.

84. Sonata Preparation Study

J. Bréval

85. Focus on Precise Rhythm

J. Werner
Duet by M. Harvey

Accelerated students may skip to No. 87.

86. Introduction to Hooked Bowing

C. Harvey

87. Hooked Bowing Etude

A. Cuccoli
Duet by M. Harvey

Accelerated students may skip to No. 89.

88. Hooked Bowing Study

C. Harvey
Duet by M. Harvey

Allegretto

89. Dotted Eighths and Regular Eighths

A. Cuccoli, arr. C. Harvey
Duet by M. Harvey

90. Hooked Bowing Intensive

H. Farmer
Duet by M. Harvey

Accelerated students may skip to No. 92.

91. Melodic Study

C. de Benito
Duet by M. Harvey

92. Dotted Eighths in 3/4 Timing

A. Cuccoli
Duet by M. Harvey

Part Seven: Left and Right Hand Training

93. Finger Agility Study

A. Cuccoli
Duet by M. Harvey

94. Agility Study

J. Alexander
Duet by M. Harvey

Accelerated students may skip to No. 97.

95. Fugal Study

Allegro Moderato

A. Nölck

96. Study on Precise Entrances

Allegretto

N. Van Rooijen

97. Study on Pickup Notes

A. Cuccoli
Duet by M. Harvey

Accelerated students may skip to No. 99.

98. Trill Study

C. Harvey
Duet by M. Harvey

99. Embellishment Study

C. Harvey
Duet by M. Harvey

100. Melodic Study in 6/8

J. B. Gross

101. String Crossing Study

S. Lee

Accelerated students may skip to No. 104.

102. Triplet Study

S. Lee

103. Agility Study

K. Paschalski
Duet by M. Harvey

104. Focus on Playing Even Notes

F. Kummer

105. Bow Agility Study

K. Davidov

106. String Crossing Etude

K. Davidov

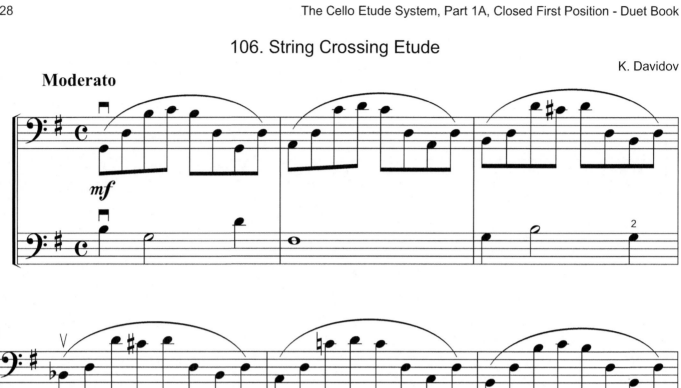

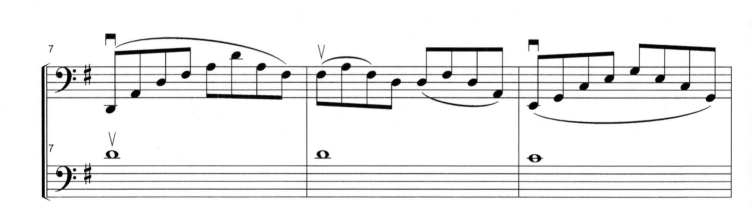

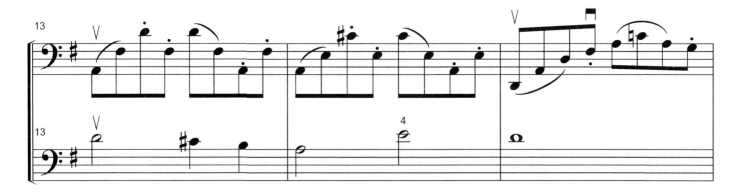

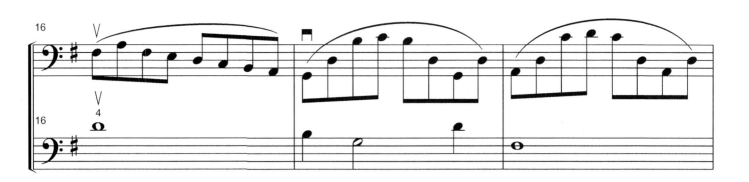

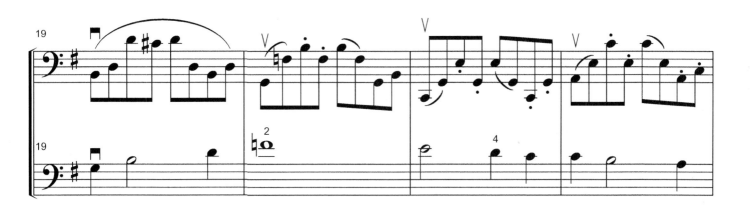

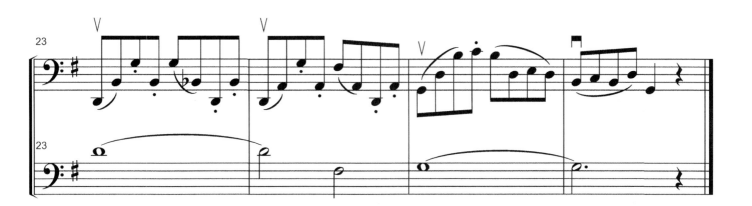

107. String Crossing

A. Nölck
Duet by M. Harvey

Allegro moderato

Accelerated students may skip to No. 108b.

108a. Melodic Etude with Rhythmic Accompaniment

D. Popper, arr. C. Harvey

108b. Melodic Etude (as Originally Written)

D. Popper

109. Learning to Slur and Hold Double Stops

- Separate Bows -

J. Borschitzky, arr. C. Harvey
Duet by M. Harvey

- With Slurs -

These two measures are played the same way.

The example on the left is the typical way of writing this double stop while the example
on the right shows how it should be played.

As you play these double stops, **the bottom note should be held** while the top note changes.

- As Written -

Accelerated students may skip to No. 110c.

110a. Double Stop Etude: Stage One

D. Popper, arr. C. Harvey

110b. Double Stop Etude: Stage Two

D. Popper, arr. C. Harvey

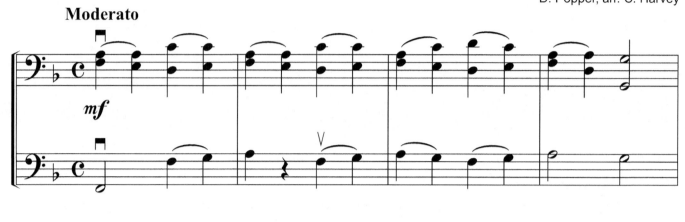

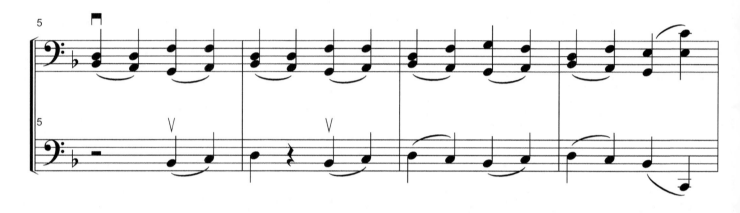

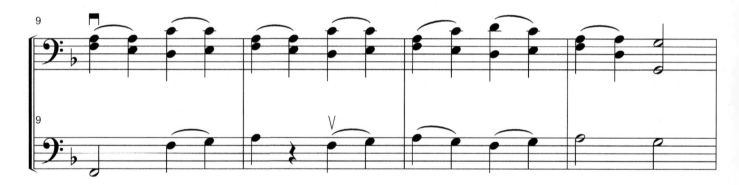

110c. Double Stop Etude: Stage Three

D. Popper, arr. C. Harvey

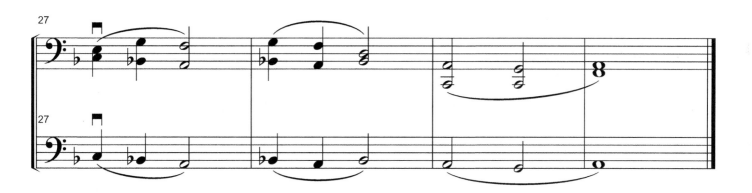

Note: Measures that are repeated within the original etude are not repeated in this exercise to avoid tiring the hand unduly.

110d. Double Stop Etude: Stage Four

D. Popper, arr. C. Harvey

♪ = 96-116   110e. Double Stop Etude: Stage Five - As Written

D. Popper

Index of Composers

Etude(s)

Index of Composers, cont.

Etude(s)

Index of Main Skills in Each Etude

Printed in Great Britain
by Amazon

19769770R00093